CREATIVE INSPIRATIONS

CATS AND DOGS

COLORING BOOK

MARJORIE SARNAT

DOVER PUBLICATIONS, INC.
MINEOLA, NEW YORK

Bibliographical Note

Cats and Dogs Coloring Book, first published by Dover Publications, Inc., in 2016, contains the following previously published Dover books: *Cats Stained Glass Coloring Book* by Ruth Soffer (2009), *Dogs Stained Glass Coloring Book* by Ruth Soffer (2010), *Creative Cats* by Marjorie Sarnat (2015), and *Dazzling Dogs* by Marjorie Sarnat (2016)

International Standard Book Number

ISBN-13: 978-0-486-80998-4
ISBN-10: 0-486-80998-6

Manufactured in the United States by RR Donnelley
80998601   2016
www.doverpublications.com

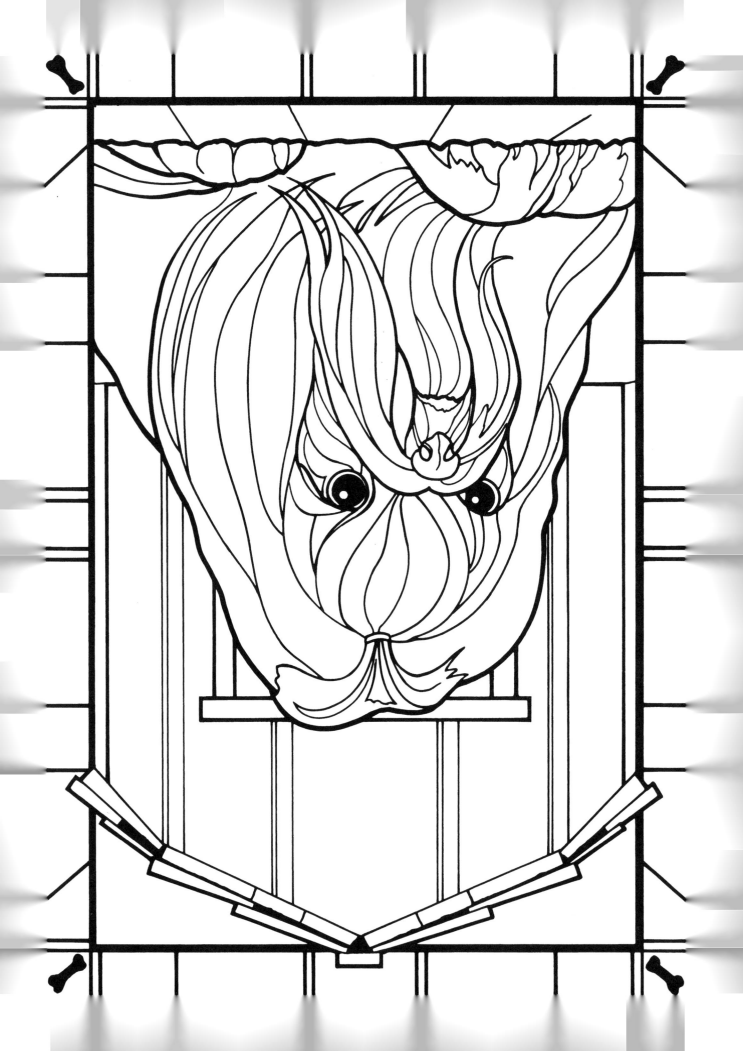

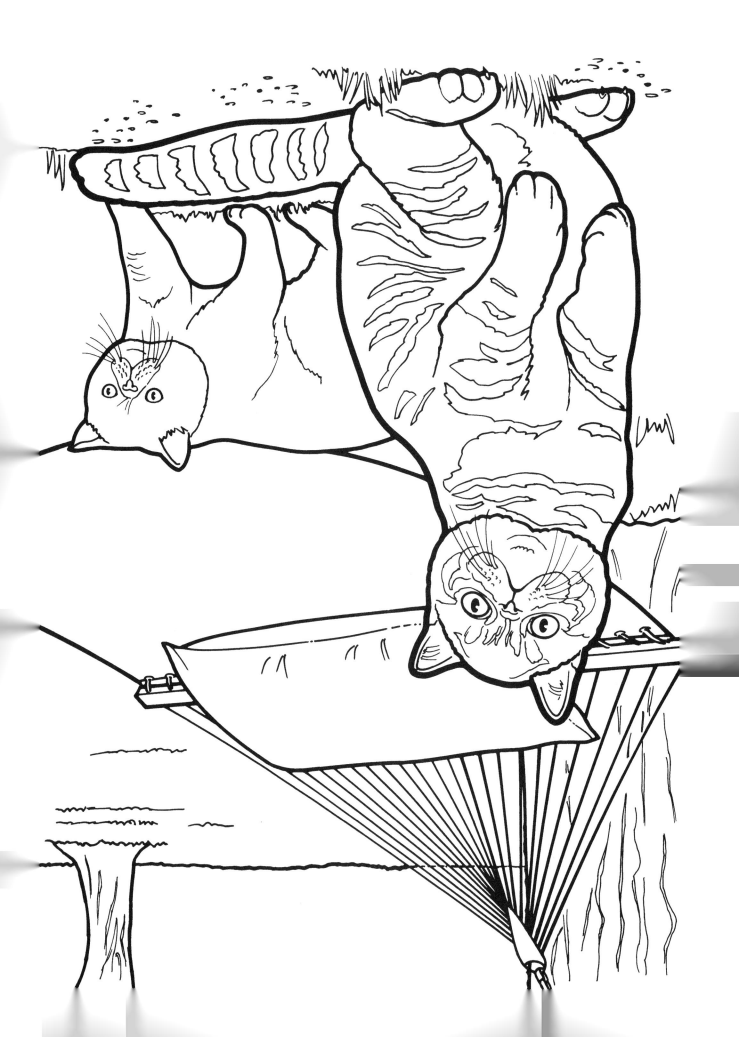

Bibliographical Note

Cats and Dogs Coloring Book, first published by Dover Publications, Inc., in 2016, contains the following previously published Dover books: *Cats Stained Glass Coloring Book* by Ruth Soffer (2009), *Dogs Stained Glass Coloring Book* by Ruth Soffer (2010), *Creative Cats* by Marjorie Sarnat (2015), and *Dazzling Dogs* by Marjorie Sarnat (2016)

International Standard Book Number

ISBN-13: 978-0-486-80998-4
ISBN-10: 0-486-80998-6

Manufactured in the United States by RR Donnelley
80998601   2016
www.doverpublications.com

CREATIVE INSPIRATIONS

CATS AND DOGS

COLORING BOOK

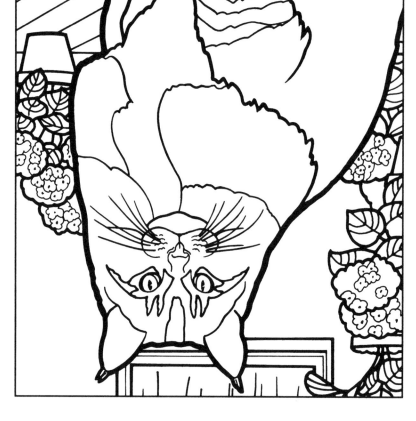

RUTH SOFFER

DOVER PUBLICATIONS, INC.
MINEOLA, NEW YORK